THE SCRABBLE® BRAND PUZZLE BOOK

Gyles Brandreth

A FIRESIDE BOOK
Published by Simon & Schuster, Inc.
New York

A Fireside Book
Published by Simon & Schuster, Inc.
Simon & Schuster Building
Rockefeller Center
1230 Avenue of the Americas
New York, New York 10020
FIRESIDE and colophon are registered trademarks of Simon & Schuster, Inc.
First published in Great Britain in 1981 by Macdonald & Co. (Publishers) Ltd.
Manufactured in the United States of America
Printed and bound by Semline, Inc.
1 2 3 4 5 6 7 8 9 10

ISBN: 0-671-50536-X

CONTENTS

Foreword / *7*

Rules for Playing the Scrabble® Brand Crossword Game / *9*

The Scrabble® Brand Puzzles / *13*

The Puzzles / *17*

The Solutions / *219*

Words Not in the Official Scrabble® Players Dictionary / *231*

FOREWORD

Scrabble® is the world's most popular brand word game. It has been around for just over half a century, but it was not invented overnight. It was developed in the fifteen-year period from 1933 to 1947 by two Americans, Alfred Butts and James Brunot. They introduced it to the American market in 1949, but it did not meet with any great success until late in 1952. During 1953 and 1954 it enjoyed a spectacular increase in popularity, and has now swept the world.

I believe I first played the Scrabble® brand crossword game in 1954 when I was six years old. I became an enthusiast when I was in my teens and attending a school called Bedales in Hampshire, England. The school's founder, John Bradley, gave me some of the most exciting and challenging bouts I have had, when I was 16 and he was 101. Invariably he won.

My passion for this game product turned into a way of life in 1971 when I launched the first British championship with respect thereto. The popularity of these championships has grown enormously over the past decade and we now have over 20,000 participants annually in regional heats throughout Great Britain, as such tournaments are sponsored by Selchow & Righter Company, owner of the registered trademark Scrabble® for a line of word and sentence game products.

This book has been specially created for Scrabble® product enthusiasts of all kinds—not just champions. It is a collection of Scrabble® brand puzzles and I hope you will enjoy them; not only are they as entertaining and challenging (and occasionally as frustrating) as good crossword puzzles, but they are a marvelously painless—indeed, I like to think splendidly pleasurable—way of improving your vocabulary and technique.

I have long considered Scrabble® to be the supreme brand word game. It is easy to play anywhere at any time, it is stimulating without being exhausting, and it keeps you alert at the age of 101. But to my mind it always had one drawback: You could never play the game on your own. But with this book, even if you don't have a partner, you can still play the Scrabble® brand crossword game—the one game in the world that now has no flaws.

RULES FOR PLAYING THE SCRABBLE® BRAND CROSSWORD GAME

Scrabble® Crossword Game is a word game for two, three or four players. The play consists of forming interlocking words, in a crossword fashion, on the Scrabble board, using letter tiles with various score values. Each player competes for the highest score by using his letters in combinations and locations that take best advantage of letter values and premium squares on the board. The combined total score for a game may range from about 500 to 1,000 or more, depending on the number of players and their skill.

TO BEGIN

All the letter tiles should be turned face down at the side of the board or thoroughly mixed in the bag provided. Players draw for first play. The player drawing the letter nearest the beginning of the alphabet plays first. The exposed tiles should then be replaced and reshuffled. Each player then draws seven new tiles and places them on his rack.

THE PLAY

1. The first player combines two or more of his letters to form a word and places them on the board to read either across or down. One letter has to be on the pink square

marked with an asterisk at the center of the board. Words cannot be played diagonally.

2. A player completes his turn by counting and announcing his score for the turn. His score (and the subsequent scores of the other players) should be recorded by one of the players. He then draws as many new letters as he has played, thus keeping seven letters on his rack.

3. The second player, and then each in turn, adds one or more letters to those already played so as to form new words. All letters played in any one turn must be placed in one row across or down the board. They must form one complete word and if, at the same time, they touch other letters in adjacent rows, they must form complete words, crossword fashion, with all such letters. The player gets full credit for all words formed or modified by his play.

4. New words may be formed by: (a) adding one or more letters to a word or letters already on the board, (b) placing a word at right angles to a word already on the board; the new word must use one of the letters already on the board or must add a letter to it, or (c) placing a complete word parallel to a word already played so that adjoining letters also form complete words.

5. The two blank tiles may be used as any letter desired. When playing a blank, the player must state what letter it represents, after which it cannot be changed during the game.

6. No letter nor a blank may be moved from the board once it has been played.

7. Any player may use his turn to replace any or all of the letters on his rack. He does so by discarding them face down, then drawing the same number of new letters, and finally mixing the discarded letters with those remaining in the pool. He then awaits his next turn to play.

8. Play continues until all the tiles have been drawn and

one of the players has used all the letters on his rack or until all possible plays have been made.

9. The rules of the game state that any words found in a standard dictionary are permitted except those starting with a capital letter, those designated as foreign words, abbreviations, and words requiring apostrophes or hyphens. These rules about the acceptability of words have been made more precise for the purpose of this book; an expanded version of the rules regarding acceptability appears in a later section, Allowed Words. Any word may be challenged before the next player starts his turn. If the word challenged is unacceptable, the player takes back his tiles and loses his turn. If the word challenged is acceptable, there is no forfeit for the challenger.

SCORING

1. One player should be selected before the game starts to keep a tally of each player's score.

2. The score value of each letter is indicated by a number at the bottom of the tile. The score value of a blank is zero.

3. *Premium Letter Squares*: A light blue square doubles the score of the letter placed on it. A dark blue square triples the score of the letter placed on it.

4. *Premium Word Squares*: The score for the entire word is doubled when one of its letters is placed on a pink square. It is tripled when a letter is placed on a red square. Include premiums for double or triple letter values, if any, before doubling or tripling the word score. If a word is formed that covers two premium word squares, the score should be doubled and re-doubled (four times the letter count), or tripled and re-tripled (nine times the letter count). Note that the center square of the board is pink, and therefore doubles the score for the first word played.

5. The score for each turn is the sum of the score values in

each word formed or modified in the play, plus the premium values resulting from placing letters on premium squares.

6. Letter and word premiums apply only in the turn in which they are first played. In subsequent turns letters count at face value only.

7. When a blank tile falls on a pink or red square, the sum of the letters in the word is doubled or tripled even though the blank itself has no score value.

8. When two or more words are formed in the same turn, each is scored. The common letter is counted, with full premium value if any, in the score for each word.

9. Any player who plays all seven of his tiles in a single turn scores a premium of 50 points in addition to his regular score for the play.

10. At the end of the game, each player's score is reduced by the sum of his unplayed letters, and, if one player has used all of his letters, his score is increased by the sum of the unplayed letters of all the other players.

THE SCRABBLE® BRAND PUZZLES

There are 200 puzzles in this book. Each puzzle represents a board at a certain stage of a game, and the seven tiles that one player has at that stage.

Here is the blank board:

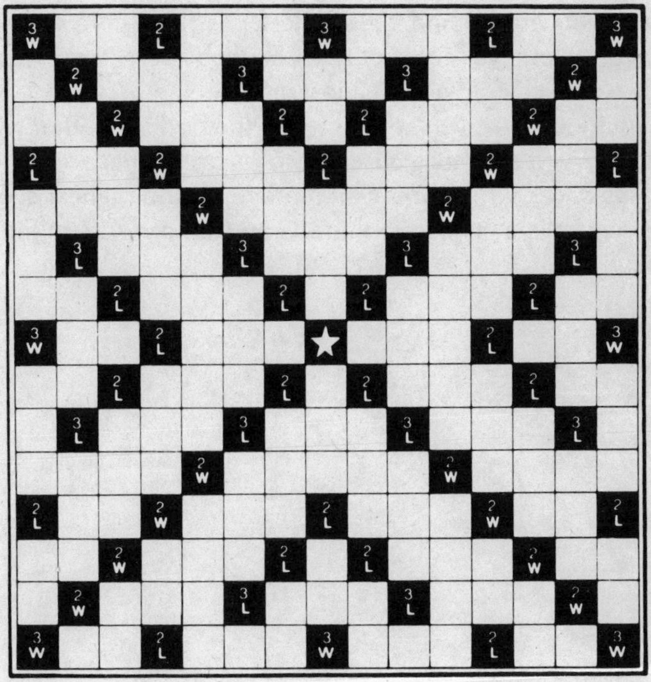

The star in the center represents the double-word-score square which must be covered in the opening move of the game.

2L	represents a double-letter-score square
3L	represents a triple-letter-score square
2W	represents a double-word-score square
3W	represents a triple-word-score square

For each puzzle, you should try to make the *highest score possible* with the given letters on the given board. In a real game, the best move might not necessarily be the move with the highest possible score. In real games, it can often be prudent to take a slightly lower score, leaving yourself with better letters for your next move. However, in the puzzles here, you are to find the highest possible score at each move. In our view the puzzles marked * are the easiest, those marked **** are the most difficult.

Solutions are given at the back of the book, together with a glossary of the more obscure words used. There may well be instances where you can improve on the highest score that we have managed to find. If you can, do write to let us know.

Letter Values

A	1	N	1
B	3	O	1
C	3	P	3
D	2	Q	10
E	1	R	1
F	4	S	1
G	2	T	1
H	4	U	1
I	1	V	4
J	8	W	4
K	5	X	8
L	1	Y	4
M	3	Z	10
		blank	0

ALLOWED WORDS

All words in these puzzles and in the solutions are from *The Official Scrabble® Players Dictionary* or the list of additional words at the back of this book. No other words are used in the puzzles; no other words should be used in your solutions.

THE PUZZLES

1. ✻

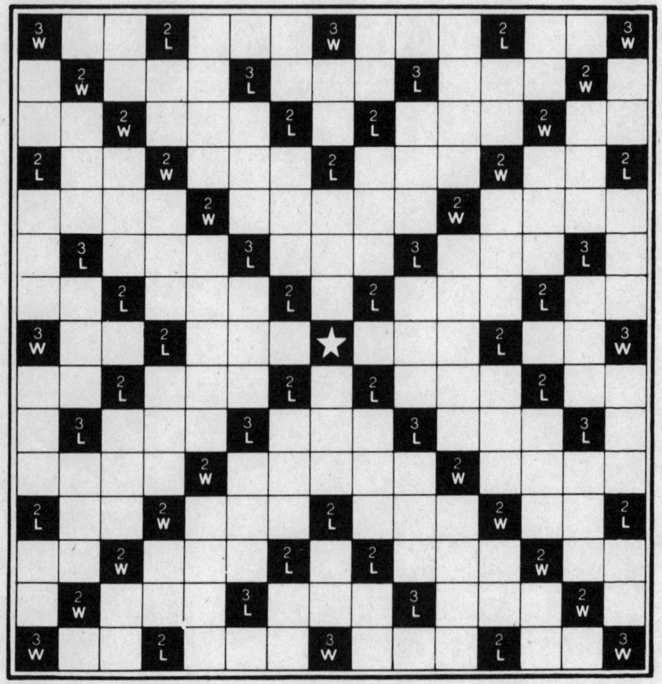

A E G I N R V

2. ✻

BOX
P TRADE
O I A
DUKE N

AEIPRST

3. **

QUAIL

EHJKOXZ

4. ✻

P
YEA
QUAD
VUG I
SEA T
X

ADEISTT

5. ✻✻

F
L
YAP
L T
QUARTO
I
CON
X
HEM
NET
W

AEIMNRT

6. ✻✻✻✻

ABEIOWZ

7. *

ME
IN
N
DIVE
M E
BYE A
A ROLE
R R
HE
A
BLOT
POT AWE

FHJKWXZ

8. ✻✻

AEINRST

9. ✻

3W			2L			J	O	W	L		2L			3W
	2W				Y	O		A	3L				2W	
		2W			A	2L		R	I	G		2W		
2L		D	2W		H		O	R		I	2W			W
		I		2W				A		D				H
Q	3L	E		P	3L	N		N	3L		I		3L	E
U	L	T	R	A	C	E	N	T	R	I	F	U	G	E
I			2L	D		B	O	A		M	2L			Z
C		2L				2L		B		A		2L	O	E
K	Y				3L			L	3L	U	N		F	
	E			2W				E		M				
2L			2W		O	V	I	N	E		2W			2L
	A	2W	T			2L		E	L			2W		
	T	E	A		3L		I	S	3L				2W	
3W		E	X	P	O	R	T	S			2L			3W

AEINRST

10. ***

F
A
E R
M
B
E E
P R O
B L E A C H N
A A O
U N T
J
O D
O

AEINRTW

11. ****

C
A
H E R
V O L E
M E
A
R
L
Y

AEGJLOU

12. ✻✻

3W			2L				3W				A			3W
	2W				3L				L	I	M	P	E	T
		2W				2L		2L	O		I	2W		
2L			2W				H	I	V	E	D			2L
				2W			I		E	2W				
	3L				P	U	K	E	R				3L	
		2L			I	2L	E	2L				2L		
3W			M	I	N	E	D				2L			3W
		2L	A		E	2L		2L				2L		
	V	I	N	E	D				3L				3L	
	O		I	2W						2W				
E	T	N	A				2L				2W			2L
	E	2W				2L		2L				2W		
	D				3L				3L				2W	
3W			2L				3W				2L			3W

ACEGLOU

13. ✻

CEGLNT□

14. ***

EEEEEEE

15. ***

ABEKOUX

16. ✻✻

3W			2L				3W				2L			3W
	2W				3L				3L				2W	
		2W				2L		2L				2W		
2L			N	I	T		2L				F			2L
				2W	E					2W	R			
	3L			B	A	Y		D	3L		I		3L	
		O	W	E		2L	B	O	V	I	N	E		
3W			H	E	A	V	Y				G			3W
		J	O			A	E	2L			E	2L		
	3L		M	U	M	P	S		3L	A	D		3L	
				2W		I				N				
2L			G	O	A	D	2L			A	2W			2L
		2W				2L		2L				2W		
	2W				3L				3L				2W	
3W			2L				3W				2L			3W

AAEEIOU

17. ***

MARC
HI HO
E PA
O
R
PECAN
O E
GAD N
O T

AEOSXYZ

18. ***

RAN
TAT
CAT
BOX
MOW
JAB
LOOK
FY
TAT
HAM
NIT

AEINORU

19. **

GRIEVING
BYE
AVARICE
OW
COLIC
LATHE
HOP
PA

AELNRRS

20. ****

I
D
BRACE E LEI
E AMAZE
O E TEG
AN N
L
E
WIS

EGNRTTU

21. **

AEINRTU

22. ***

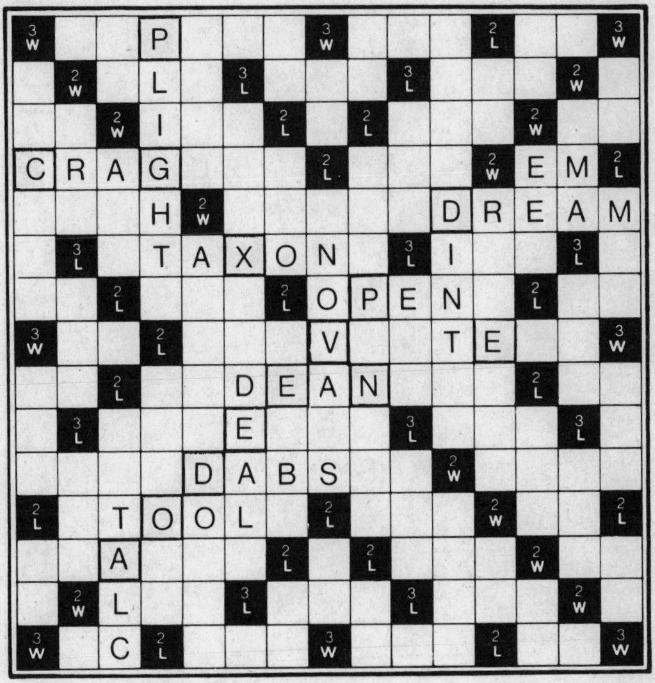
P
L
I
C R A G E M
H D R E A M
T A X O N I
O P E N N
V T E
D E A N
E
D A B S
T O O L
A
L
C

AEINRST

23. ✻✻

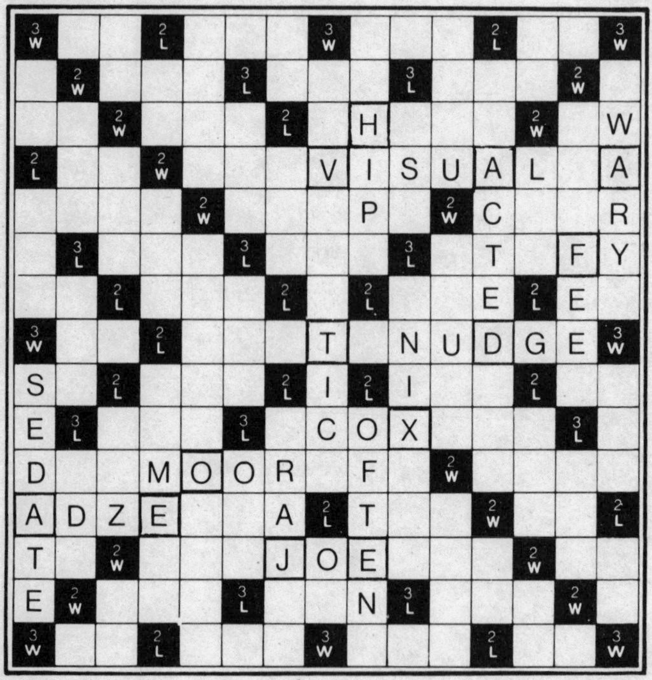

DIORSTT

24. ✻✻✻

THOSE
EXPORT
RELET
EVINCING
MOURN
DREAMING
INSET
OATHS
PELVIS
ERIC
TIDIED

AAAAAAA

25. ✻

F
YO A
WIDER HAY
EMIT

DEEIIJV

26. ✻

EEOQTUY

27. ✻

ADEILNR

28. ****

CEIKPRS

29. *

H I D E
O
B O
T

AEINOUV

30. ✻

QUA
QUIN

ADEGSTY

31. ****

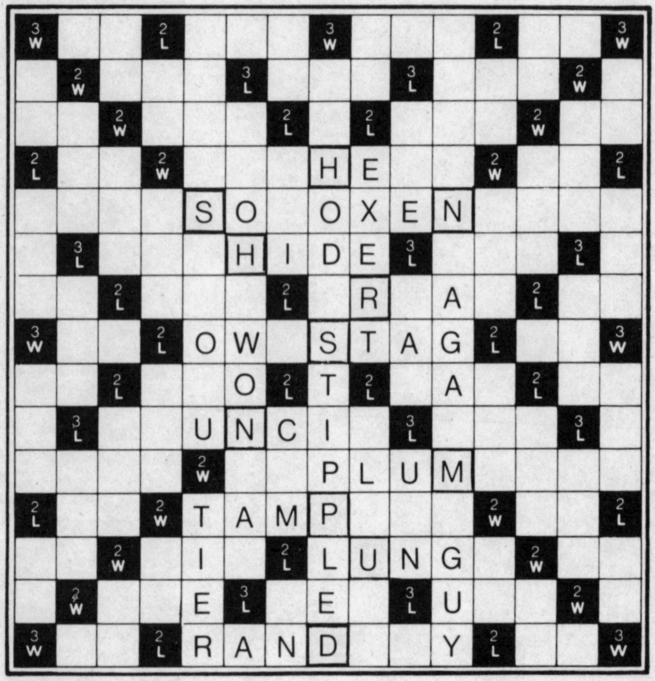

HE
SO OXEN
HIDE
R A
OW STAG
O T A
UNCI
PLUM
TAMP
I LUNG
E E U
RAND Y

BBEILSY

32. ***

FOAM
ANTE
IT
N A
ARC L
AX OO
OD T IN
WHEELING
G K
OOLOGY E
I E D

CHILORZ

33. ✻✻

DIME
WARE
MATE
FINE
TART
BANE
NONE
PARK
CAGE

ADEFTY□

34. ***

JOWLS
WIT
ADO
ZONES
EWE
YEAR
YE
REVS

ABCGHKO

35. ✻✻

FHKPWY□

36. ✻

GUM
RAT
EN
AM I
ECHOIC
X A

AELNRTU

37. ****

A
ZAX
MO
MOO
E
PA
GAN
U

KLNRRTT

38. ✻

E
P
E
A E
A N
A N N A
A N A
I N
A E O N

AHLOPRT

39. ✻✻✻✻

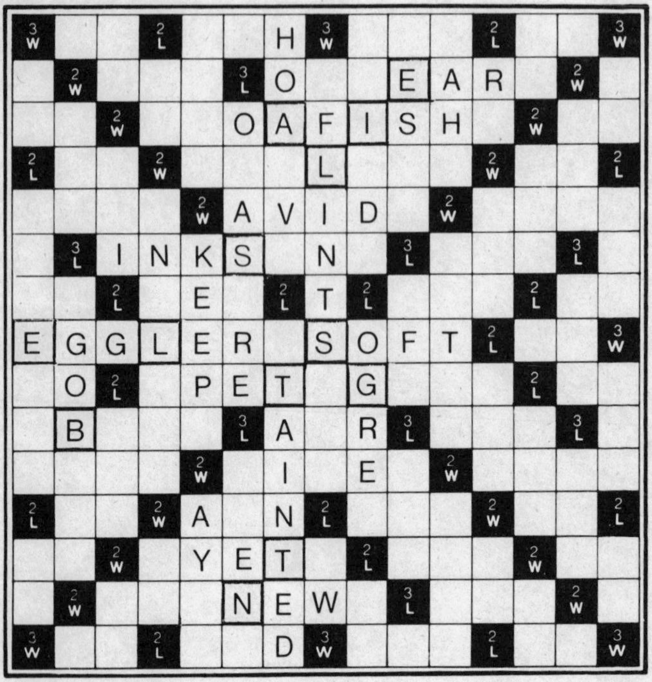

AEJNORZ

40. ****

3W		P	I		E		3W		R	A	T	I	O	3W
R	2W		T		V				E				2W	
A	H	2W	E		O	2L		2L	P			2W		
N	O	R	M	A	L		Q		L		2W			2L
				2W	V		U		I	2W		F	L	Y
	3L				E	Y	E		C	O	Z	E	3L	
R	O	T	U	N	D	2L	A	I	A			D		
3W			2L			E	N				2L			3W
		2L				D		2L				2L		
S	O	C	K	I	N	G			3L				3L	
T				2W		I				2W		F	I	B
A			2W			N	2L				2W	I		2L
B		2W		W	A	G	G	E	D			X		
	2W			H	3L				O			E	2W	
3W			S	O	M	E	3W		T	A	R	S		3W

ARSTU□□

41. ✻

B
HOB
MAY
H
FOP

AJOOWWY

42. ✻

N
E G
W O O L
Q U O T H
F
F

AABDRTU

43. **

CEEKPTW

44. ✻✻

G
THE
COOEY
F WOMB
I WOMB
GREVE
H E
T N

ADLNRTY

45. ✻✻

Z
FURY O
O DAH
OES I O
PRIVATE
ALA U
R D
T I
A T
N

BEGIJNR

46. ***

AEMRSTY

47. ✻

C O Y E R
L E A U
F A B N
M A T
P A X

ADHNORU

48. ✻✻

PHENIC
A O
T T
HE O
A JO
ASOCIAL
U K R
D V
QUID E
U B Y
I L
N E

AERRSSS

49. **

PHEW B
VIOLATE
E ELD Y
IF
NAP
ERA
DOT

AELNSST

50. ✻

AJMNTUY

51. **

CLAWING
LAX
PIED
WEIR
BELLOW
AID
WOVEN
MEEK
EYED
GRIME
BUNNY
BROUGHT
ZONE
HAP

AEORSST

52. ****

AAIMNV□

53. ✻✻✻

AHA
KID
DYE
GEL
MOO
ANA
TOR
ICE
BOB
OHO
W

IPSTXY□

54. ✻

OHMIC
BEAT
ORT
E

EGIJNST

55. **

AEORTVX

56. **

BE
BARED
A
FLINCH
ILIA
MO R
AT
PA

ELORSTV

57. ✻✻

AEEHHWW

58. *

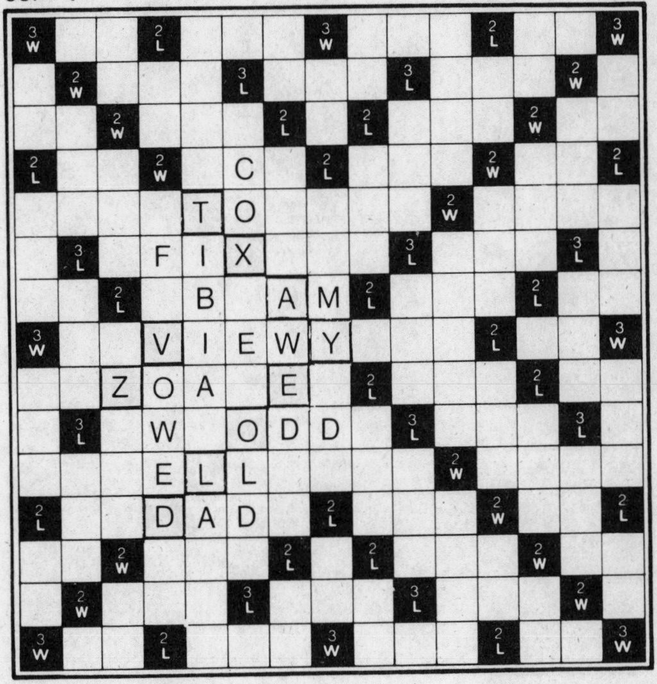
C
TO
FIX
B AM
VIEWY
ZOA E
W ODD
ELL
DAD

EHKMNRY

59. ****

BELNOYZ

60. **

HOPE
LEA E O R
STATE TE
A E I

ACGINOR

61. ***

BFLMNRT

62. ✻

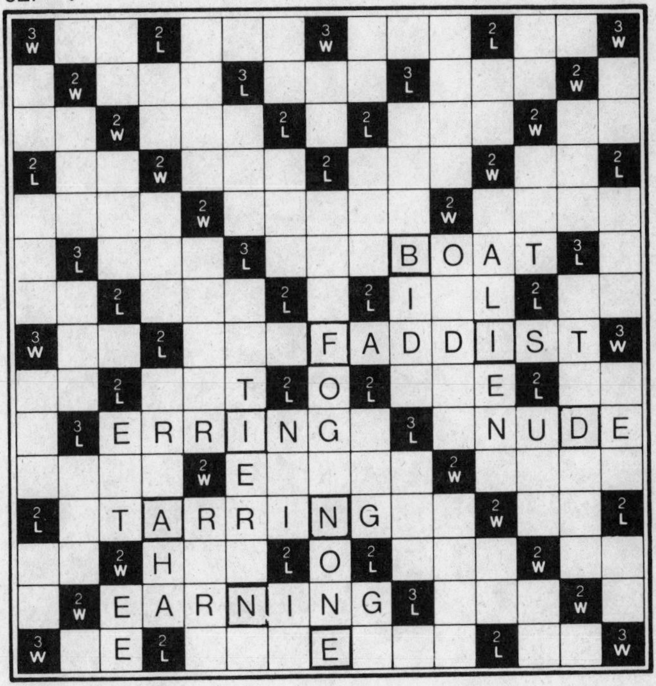
BOAT
FADDIST
ERRING
NUDE
TARRING
EARNING

HIKSVWY

63. ✻✻

AEHMMWY

64. ***

O R E E
E N A
GANDER
M I NA
NEON I
TAR G T

ADEILSY

65. ✻

H O
A W E V E I N
E X P E R T
P N A T
O D D
H E R
A T
T

AAEEIOU

66. ✻✻✻

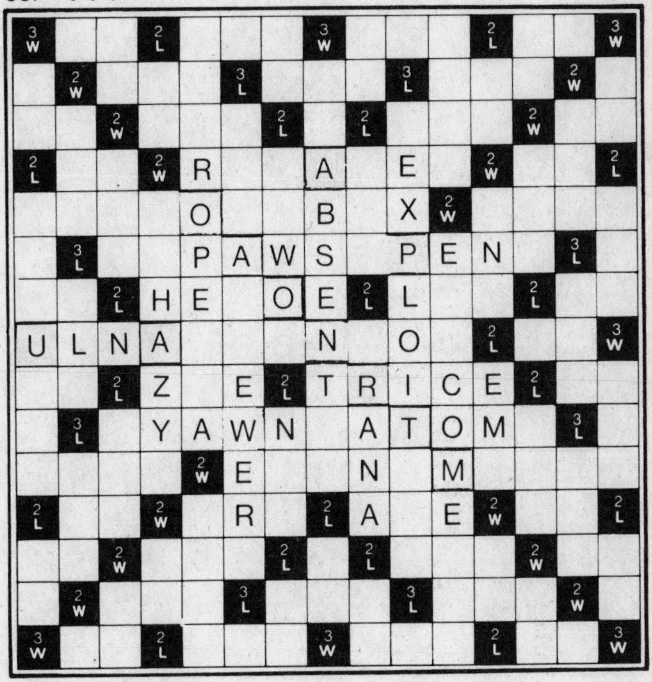

R A E
O B X
PAWS PEN
HE OE L
ULNA N O
Z E TRICE
YAWN ATOM
E N M
R A E

ABCDEFQ

67. **

AEHOQST

68. ***

E DOOR
ASTERN
T NEED
RID
M
EARTH V
T I A
E PUKE
P I
JAUNTY L
O O
BOOM

EHINTXZ

69. ***

3W			L				3W			D	2L			3W
	2W		A		3L				3L	R			2W	
		2W	C			2L		S	P	A	N	N	E	R
M	O	T	E	T	T	S	2L			G	2W			2L
				2W	O					O				
	3L				A	D	J	O	I	N			3L	
		2L			D	2L		2L		S		2L		
3W			2L		Y	A	P				2L			3W
		2L				2L	R	2L			I	2L		
	3L				3L		O		3L		C	H	I	V
	E			B	R	O	W	N		2W	O			
B	E	L	L	Y			2L	A	L	O	N	G		2L
		2W	E			2L		2L		V		2W		
	2W		F		3L				3L	E			2W	
3W			T				3W			R	2L			3W

ADEINST

70. ***

EN
O
ANN
A
Z
LIGHT
R O
OB
TA
S
E
ES

EENSTV□

71. ✻✻✻

AEIOUVV

72. ✻✻✻✻

TOOLING
NOTIONS
TWEET
WIG
FIFER
DIGIT
FIN
FIN
AS
AI

DEHNOTZ

73. ✻

R
Y
ULE
WEBBING
ERA
E
H
K
HER

AFGMPTW

74. ✻✻✻

B
L
I
M
PROEM
FA
F
I
EPICURE
RETSINA E

ABCELRS

75. ✻✻

L A G E R
A O B I T
N K Y E
O
L
I
N

EEEHVWZ

76. ***

AEHOSTZ

77. ✻✻

L I
L M
HARP
M U
EARLY
S
RODE
V
WAN OUR
ELAND

ENSSSTU

78. ✻✻✻

3W			2L				3W				2L			3W
	2W				3L				3L				2W	
		2W				2L		2L			P	2W		
2L			2W				2L		F	O	H			2L
				2W	V				L	2W	O	N	E	
	3L		L	E	I		B	A	Y				R	
		2L	A		M	E	U	2L				2L	R	
3W			D				M	A	R		2L			3W
		2L			L	2L		2L	I			2L		
	3L		E	R	E		C	O	G				3L	
				2W	T	E	A			2W				
2L			2W				D	I	N		2W			2L
		2W				2L		2L				2W		
	2W				3L				3L				2W	
3W			2L				3W				2L			3W

AGHNOPR

79. **

CDEORTW

80. ***

CEFORRS

81. ✻✻

APPLE
RELAX
ORATE
MINER
ALERT

BDHMNST

82. **

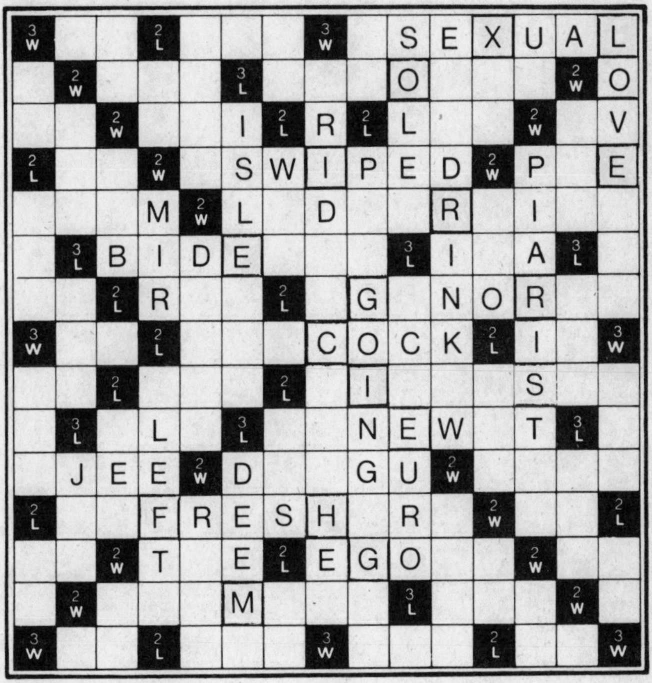
SEXUAL
O O
I R L V
SWIPED P E
M L D R I
BIDE I A
R G NOR
COCK I
I S
L NEW T
JEE D GU
FRESH R
T E EGO
M

AAAAAEI

83. **

PIXIE
I N
L I R
TABOO GO
R E TE L
TI E S
P N

ACDENRS

84. **

ACDEIRY

85. **

Z J
A N A
X K

AEHLNOT

86. ***

MINED
PAGED

AEHLNOT

87. ✻✻✻

AEINQTU

88. ✻

JOYOUS
A
A M
ANTE

ABKLRTZ

89. **

I
DROP
TE
A
L
RE
E
WHO

FGHMOPW

90. ✻✻✻

HMNOPYY

91. ***

RIFE
O
QUA
X
T
WHILE
H
I
S
ROMPED
D
LAW
M
YET
YET
E
E
T
FEAT

AEINRST

92. ✻

QUINA
QUEAN

FHKMPWY

93. **

IRE
AT
POI

AELTVWZ

94. **

CFIILM□

95. ✻✻

AEHRSVW

96. **

C
TAP
MIMIC
LATERAL
SATURATES
RELATED
DATER
RED
D

BEIKSY□

97. *

P
E N D I
E O A N
B U N
R
M I
A N
E A U

ECIKRTW

98. ✻✻✻

A I R
G
A T E
I N
R
E
N E E D L E S

AEHINRS

99. **

B
U
WENT
IGLOO CAD
ADD N H
C THE
EE ER
R
PER

AILMSYZ

100. ****

CNRTUY□

101. ✻

ECHOIC
L E REEK
MI PA
T
GET
O A
BO

EIMRSWX

102. ✻

W
AD
WISE
OO TA
ER
D

BHMNOTU

103. **

NEON
NOW
DEW
DRUG
DOG
DEW
ROW
ROOM

ABEKOOZ

104. **

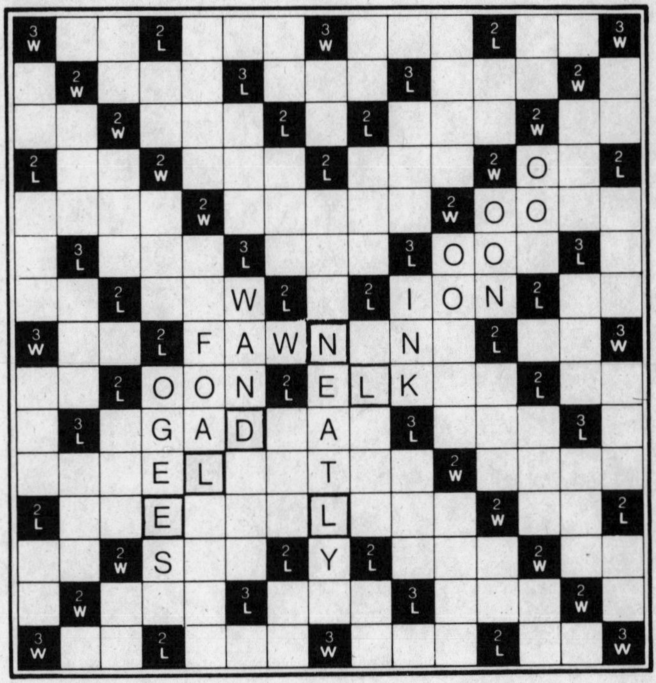

ABERRTZ

105. **

B E
T A B O O
A O O
I N Z
Y K Y
A E A
C O W E R
A H E
T

HLMNPRR

106. ****

ABDHMOR

107. ✻

J
I
N E A T
X E R I C
E T E
S O Y

ABDHMOR

108. ***

RATE
A I
CHI T
K R
O
P U
ZEBUB
JOG L
O E
E
YO

AEFIRST

109. ***

D O P
SNOOKERED
DOER A
RID
PAWS L
LA OBEY
AGO
T

AEFNRYZ

110. ✻

F A
O X
Q U E S T
U S
A

DEGHKOT

111. ***

E
A NAMES
I U
R T P
YO O R
Y T K E
E A A M
RELATION
X R T E O
H C A WIN
O L
R I
T FACE
A

DEHOPRZ

112. ✻✻

ALOQRSU

113. **

3W			2L				3W				2L			3W
	2W				3L				3L				2W	
		2W				2L		2L				2W		
2L			2W				2L			Z	O			2L
				V	E	T		D	S	O				
	3L		B	O	3L		B	O	3L	E	A		3L	
		2L		L	E	V	A	2L	Y	A	H	2L		
3W			2L		R		U	P			2L			3W
		2L				2L	D	U	O			2L		
	3L				3L			M	3L	O			3L	
				2W			D	A	M	E				
2L			2W				I				2W			2L
		2W				O	R	2L				2W		
	2W				3L	U	G		3L				2W	
3W			2L			T	E				2L			3W

AEEHRTW

114. **

AEHLNRT

115. ✻✻✻

COVETS
P TANGENT
ARKS E
W L

AAIQTU☐

116. ✻

I S
S Q U A R E
S Q U I R E

DHKTWYZ

117. **

ADEGOTV

118. ***

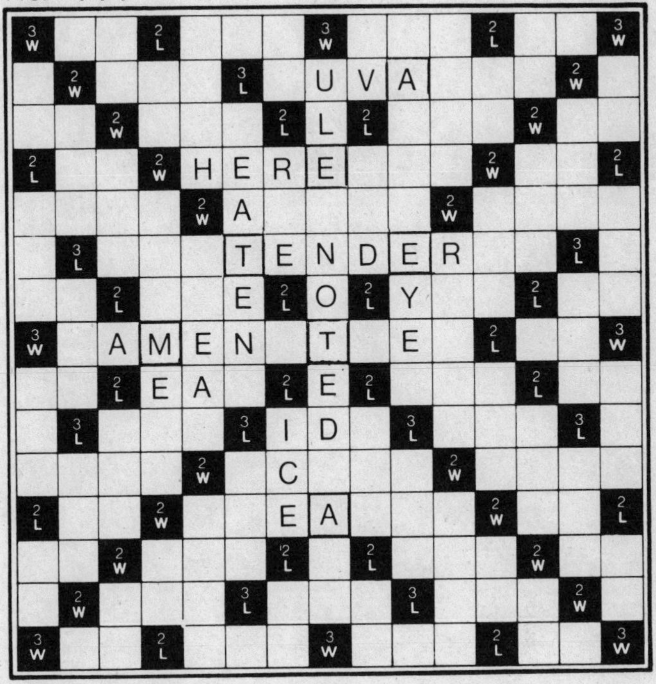

EINRSTY

119. ***

O O
A D
R I D E I
C O T
T A I
B
E H
L A T E

ABEPRST

120. ✻✻

LNOUWXY

121. ✻✻

POLO U S ABLE
REPAINT
W
TORNADO
A A G A
VEER T E ROUX

EEELNSV

122. *

G
FED
JAM
TUN
DUG
WOP
VET
BOY
ZEL
CON
O

ABEIRSW

123. ✻✻

A
R
J O K E
O X
O B

DEIPRST

124. ****

RAGG
RAUN
VULN
VALI
TITI
TAAL

ADHKORW

125. ✻

P
E
F L O G
C O D O
B O I L P H U T
R O A
V I E W
V A G U E K A R T
R W
E A
J A Y Y E
Z O L
M

EIRSSST

126. ✻✻

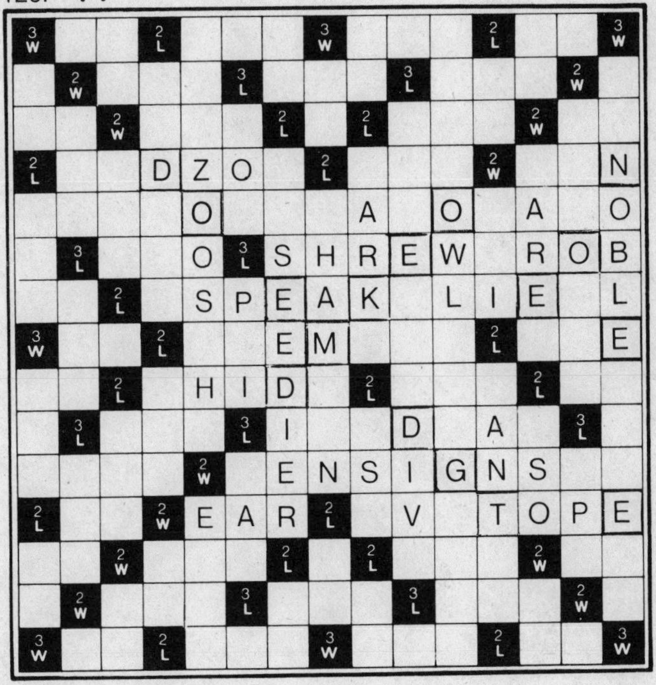
DZO N
O A O A O
O SHREW ROB
SPEAK LIE L
EM E
HID
I D A
ENSIGNS
EAR V TOPE

ACEELYY

127. **

WHIZ GO
IO O EA
DEFIANT
EDICT C
E A
KA
IRATE
I

ALLSTXY

128. *

BARKED
EXCITING
BLISTER
GAZE
AWED
BEEN
DELETED
DRIVE
EYED

OOOOOOO

129. ****

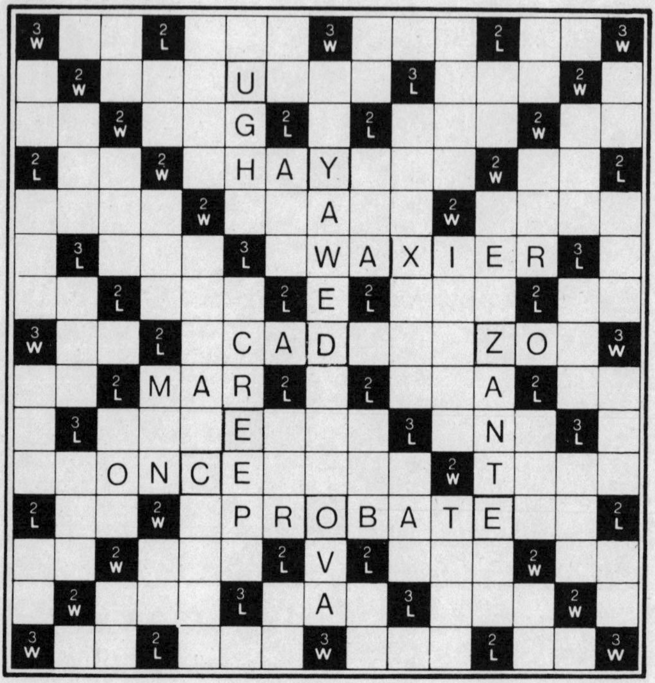
U
G
HAY
A
WAXIER
E
CAD ZO
MAR A
E N
ONCE T
PROBATE
V
A

AGKLOST

130. ✻

F
WEALD
DOOR
BALLOON
R
A
C
HEFT

AEGHMWY

131. ✻✻

O
OCA
TAPE
A
W

DEIIRST

132. ✻

HOLE
CANAL
CAP
DEEP
DEFT
TAR
URINO
FAWN
NO
REALISM
AVA
MA

ABCLOTT

133. **

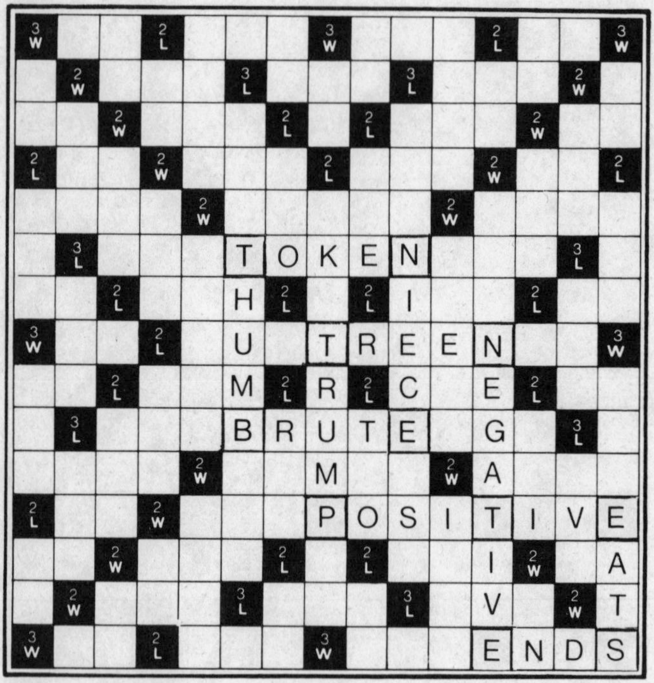
TOKEN
TREEN
BRUTE
POSITIVE
ENDS

CEELORT

134. ✻✻✻

LING
OR B V
DEARIE
E A N
COL T
O
RE
NA

CEELORT

135. ✻

O
HAZEL
ORAL
LAAGER
I
T

AHIKSTW

136. ✻✻✻

CHILSTY

137. ✻

OVATE
SCAR
RUN
T
SNOW

BILLOWY

138. ✻✻

YE
WE
TE
RE
OE
ME
HE
EE
BE
AE
E

AINPSTV

139. **

AFKMPTW

140. ✻

3 W 2 L 3 W 2 L 3 W
2 W 3 L 3 L 2 W
2 W 2 L 2 L 2 W
2 L 2 W 2 L 2 W 2 L
2 W 2 W
3 L 3 L 3 L 3 L
2 L 2 L 2 L 2 L
3 W 2 L 2 L 3 W
2 L 2 L 2 L 2 L
3 L 3 L 3 L 3 L
2 W 2 W
2 L 2 W 2 L 2 W 2 L
2 W 2 L 2 L 2 W
2 W 3 L 3 L 2 W
3 W 2 L 3 W 2 L 3 W

EFIPRX□

141. ✻✻

A
N
DOZE
V
E
RATE
X
E

AEIORSV

142. ✻✻✻

A
N
DOPE
V
E
RATE

AEINORS

143. ***

END
DEWY
EVER
RATE

ADEIORS

144. ***

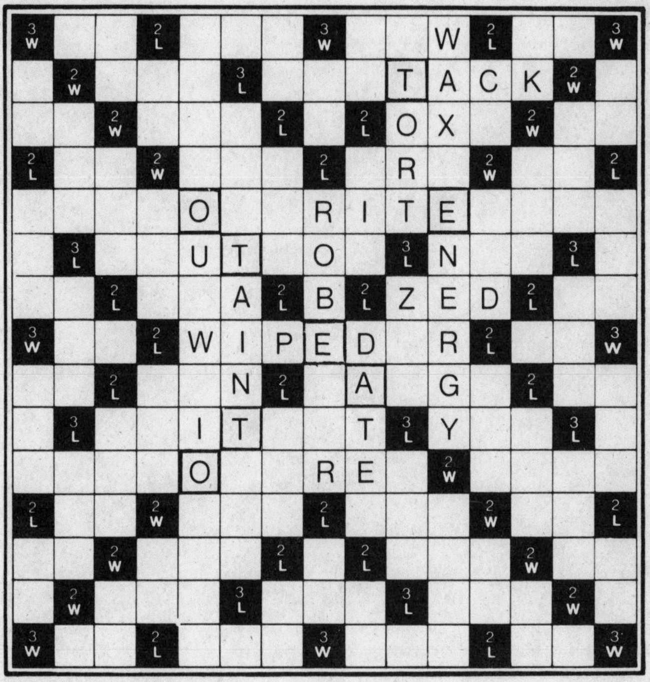

DEGORSS

145. ✻✻

ABGIKNR

146. ✻✻

R R
A E A
I F E E T
B A N A N A
O T
O P E N S H A R E
O

ADKMOVY

147. ***

INOPTUZ

148. ✻

ROTOR

ABENOVX

149. ***

3W			2L				3W	A	G	E	N	T		O
	2W				3L			N	3L			O	A	F
		2W				2L	B	A	S	E		2W		
2L			2W				2L	T			2W			2L
				2W				H		Z				
	3L				3L		T	E	N	O	R		3L	
		2L				2L		M				2L		
3W			2L				B	A	L	A	N	C	E	S
		2L				2L	A	2L				2L		
	3L				3L		T	A	L	L	I	E	S	
				2W			T			I			I	
2L			2W				E			N	2W		R	2L
		2W				2L	R	E	V	O	L	V	E	S
	2W				3L	O	Y		3L				D	O
3W	F	A	R	R	O	W	3W				2L			X

CENORTU

150. ✻

T
BAR
MOPED
GET
D

DEGINRT

151. ✻✻

H
A
A Y A H
A
Y

DEIRSTU

152. **

C R A S H
O W
E A M
M

EHILNTX

153. ✻✻

DEILRST

154. ✻

RUSH
RASH

BCHKMUW

155. ✻

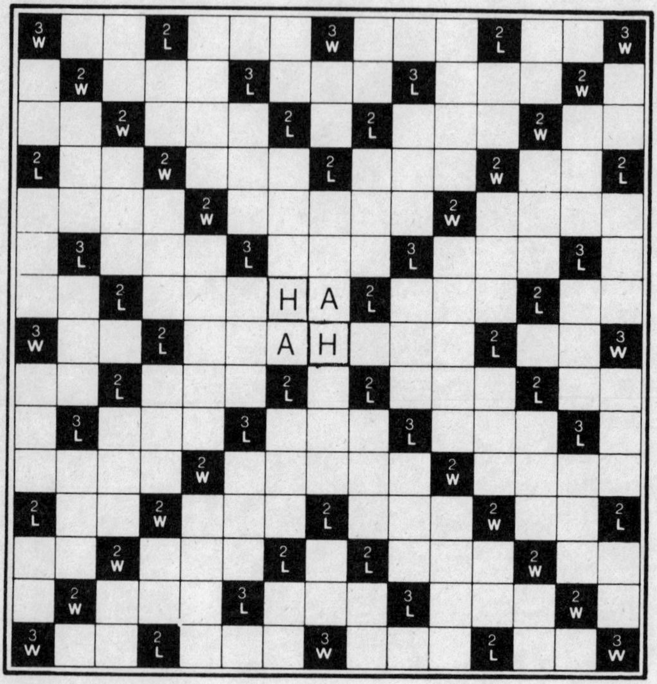

AELRRST

156. ✻

HUM
REGAL
SHY

ADEIVWZ

157. ✻✻

E
U R

AELRSTV

158. ✻

GGHIINN

159. ***

CHIPSSY

160. ✻

L
SKIP
M M
LOVE
G

ADGRTVY

161. **

LA
COY
A
MAR
ODE
W
SKID

AEORSTT

162. ***

FOCI
BLITZ
BERTH
ZONED
EVER
NOTE
HOPED
PLOY

GIMNSTY

163. ✻✻✻

EARTH
CHIEF
TOMATO
COLON

AFGIORT

164. ****

BATE I L
R DRAG
CAFE RAGGED
OO A V
L R E

ACDILMO

165. ✻✻

AEHMORX

166. ✻✻

HEM
FOUNT
RADIO
EARTH
BANJ
HEART
FORTH
ELM

AKLOPRT

167. ✻✻

T
TOFFS
ANA

AGHINSU

168. ***

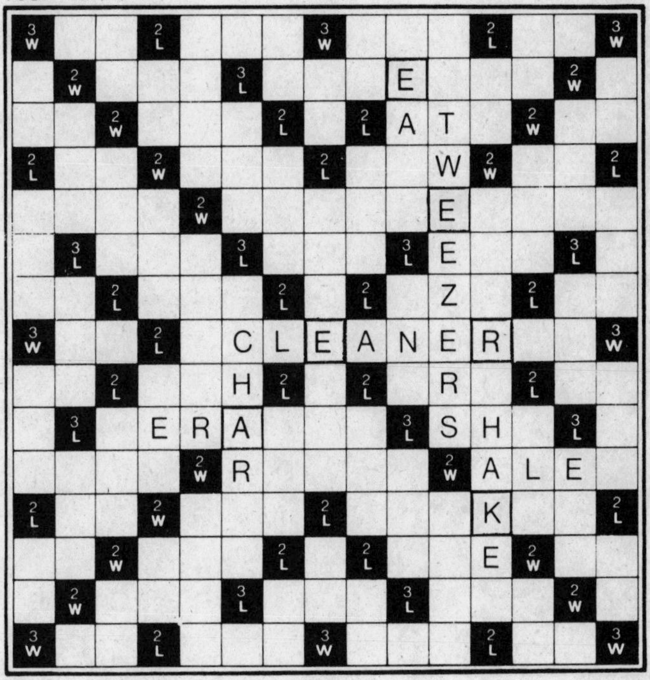
E
A T
W
E
E
Z
C L E A N E R
H R
E R A S H
R A L E
K
E

GJLNOUY

169. ✻✻

3W			2L				3W				2L			3W
	2W				3L				3L				2W	
		2W				2L		2L				2W		
2L			2W				2L				2W			2L
				2W				V		2W				
	3L				M		B	E	Y				3L	
		2L		R	E	2L	O	X	E	N		2L		
C			W	O	U	N	D		A		2L			3W
L		F	O	E		2L	E	H				2L		
A	L	A	E		3L			A	T				3L	
N		H		2W				D	A	M				
K	A		2W				2L	J		O	N			2L
I		2W				2L		2L		L	A	G		
N	O				3L				3L	E		O	W	E
G			2L				3W				2L		E	A

CDEGNRT

170. ✻✻✻

CHLMRTW

171. ***

CDEIRST

172. ✻✻

WOG
RID
J R
LOVED
GID
A
LOX

ABCFHWY

173. ***

ACGHNTY

174. **

O	H		2L				3W				2L		F	A
B	I	Z			3L				3L			N	I	X
		O				2L		2L			S	2W	V	
2L	W	A	D				2L			M	I	R	E	2L
			I	T						A	R	E		
H	O	V	E	R	3L		M	A	T	T	E	D	3L	
E	R	2L		A		K	A	T		E	S	2L		
W	E		F	I	N	E	D				2L			3W
		2L		L		Y		2L				2L		
	3L		G	I	O				3L				3L	
			A	N	D					2W				
2L		P	U	G			2L				2W			2L
		I	N			2L		2L				2W		
	Y	E	T		3L				3L				2W	
C	O	R	S				3W				2L			3W

BCEGLNR

175. ***

3W			2L				C	A	R	B	I	N	E	3W
	2W				3L		O		3L		A		2W	
		2W				2L	N	2L			M	2W		
2L			2W				T	E			B	L	E	W
				2W			R			2W				E
	3L				3L		A		3L				3L	T
I		2L			E	2L	C	2L		H		2L		
T	E	D	I	U	M		T	R	E	A	S	U	R	E
		2L	N		I	2L		O		L		2L		
	3L				R	I	P	E		L			3L	
				2W						O				
2L			2W				2L				2W			2L
		2W				2L		2L				2W		
	2W				3L				3L				2W	
3W			2L				3W				2L			3W

FORSWYZ

176. **

GRIM
GREEN
DRAB
DEAF
FRUMP
BLACK
COIN
ABRUPT
NOTED
ADROIT
TELLING

AEFHILY

177. ✻✻

3W		C	A	P		H	3W	Y			F	A	N	3W
	2W			A	3L	E	V	E	3L		I		2W	W
		2W		R		2L	E	2L		A	B	O	D	E
2L			2W	I			T	E	S	T	2W		U	2L
				T						2W			O	F
	3L			I	3L				3L				3L	I
T	A	C	H	E		2L		2L				2L	O	R
3W	X		2L	S	U	N	S				L	A	D	3W
N	E	T				2L	O	2L			A	2L		
	3L			T	R	O	U	B	L	E	D		3L	
			L	O				L		2W				G
2L			I				2L	A			M	O	O	R
Q	U	I	N			2L		Z			A	2W		I
	2W		E		3L			E	3L		N		2W	P
3W	M	I	R				3W	D	I	V	E	R	S	3W

EGGKNWY

178. **

D
E N D
A L A
I
V
E H
R U G
R U T
T R
I
P

EEEIRST

179. ✻

EHLMTYY

180. ✻✻✻

R
E
L
A
F T O T
E L O P E W O E F U L
X I
P U N
R
E
T
T
Y

DHIORTY

181. ***

O
N
C
O N C E
O
O

GILNNUV

182. ✻

E
BAN
OO
H

ACDEFPX

183. ✻

ADHOOTZ

184. ✻

ART
EE
HEAVE
I
WON
ROE
Y

AACFGNP

185. ✻✻✻✻

TABOO
WHOLE
GAUDY
AXED
TRAINEE
TAR
ERA
GALA
DEAD
EXPERT

CENOSTU

186. ✻

ADKMPSU

187. ***

VYING
GINGER
GRAVE

ADEILOT

188. ✻✻

AIORTYZ

189. ✻

ZEBRAS
BOX
RE
ANVILS
AFIRE
LATRINES
FAIR
REE
EEN

DGOPTWY

190. ***

N
F A I R
V
H A I R
E L
E
D O A
B A R
T

EENRSTY

191. ***

B O
U R
G R E E D
W
E
T I T R A T E
A L E A
E L
C

ACDHIMR

192. ✻✻✻

E G I L N S W

193. ✻✻✻

COOPWXY

194. ✻

ABBHQUY

195. ✻✻✻✻

3W	M		2L				3W				C	H	I	3W
	U				3L		A		A	I	A		2W	
	T	2W				2L	I	N	N		N	2W		
B	E	T	T	E	R	E	D				D			2L
E			A	2W						2W	I	O	N	S
G	3L		W		3L		N		3L		E		3L	
		2L	S			B	E	L	T	E	D	2L		
3W	O	R	E			A	T				2L			3W
		2L				L		2L		G	R	I	T	
	3L				3L	E	H		3L	O			3L	
S				2W			A	V	I	D				
E			P	E	R	I	L				2W			2L
Z	E	R	O			2L	L	2L				2W		
	2W		R		3L		O	F	3L				2W	
3W			K				3W				2L			3W

ACNPSW□

196. ***

3W			2L				3W				2L			3W
	2W				3L				3L				2W	
		2W				2L	U	G		G		2W		
2L			2W				2L	A		A	2W			2L
				2W				L		R		N		
	3L			P	3L		B	A	M	B	O	O	3L	
		2L		E		2L	O	2L	A		W	2L		
3W			2L	C	O	A	X		D		E			3W
		2L			A	2L	E	2L				2L		
	3L	H	U	N	K		S	T	A	I	R		3L	
		E		2W				O		2W	E			
2L			2W				2L				2W			2L
		2W				2L		2L				2W		
	2W				3L				3L				2W	
3W			2L				3W				2L			3W

EIOVWYZ

197. *

LIGHT

ABCEJOT

198. **

E R I C
P N O
F U E L R
A B B A E E
R

ACGILMX

199. ✻✻

EHILRST

200. ****

AIRTUX□

THE SOLUTIONS

1. Play VINEGAR for 80 points. The V must be on a double-letter-score square. REAVING will not do, as the most it can score is 76 points.
2. Play PARTIES, UP, KA, TIER and BEANS for 118 points. Do not play PASTIER, PIASTRE, PIRATES or TRAIPSE.
3. Using the I of QUAIL, play JIZ for 37 points.
4. Play QUADS, IT, TA and STATED for 30 points.
5. Play MINARET, ICON, and AHEM for 89 points.
6. Play BWAZI, PROA and YETI for 70 points.
7. Play JINX for 36 points.
8. Using the L of REEL, play ENTRAILS for 131 points; or using the E of LIVE, play TRAINEES for 131 points also.
9. Play QUICKS and SERIN for 31 points.
10. Play TINWARE, EEN, PROW and NA for 104 points.
11. Using ME, play MEGAJOULE for 87 points.
12. Play CAGOULE and MANIAC for 72 points.
13. Using the blank as an E, play NEGLECT and PRIME for 85 points.
14. Play EXEGETES and RE for 68 points.
15. Play BEAUX and BHANG for 99 points. XYLEM and XERIC for 93 points is good, but not the best!

16. Play EUGOI, GU, OO and AI (under GOAD) for 15 points.
17. Using the O of POD and the A of GAD, play ZAXES, ZO and OX for 83 points.
18. Play URINE and RANI for 22 points.
19. Play SNARLER, LATHEN and PAR for 80 points.
20. Play GRUTTEN and MENU for 88 points. Other high-scoring moves involve the words BUTTERING, GUTTERING and UTTERING.
21. Play UNITER, JOT and ONE for 25 points. While this is the highest-scoring move, it would probably not be the best move in a real game. The best move is probably to play one letter, creating an opening, and hoping that you will then be able to use it to play a seven-letter word on the next move. Playing the A, and using the H of DOH, to make HA, is such a move.
22. Using the C of TALC, play NACRITES for 149 points.
23. Play DISTORT and SEDATED for 104 points.
24. Play TARAMASALATA for 60 points.
25. Play JIVED, REV, ME, and HID for 57 points.
26. Using the U of VIRTU, play QUOTE for 48 points.
27. Using the V of VIA, play either VAILED or VARIED for 33 points.
28. Play RIPECKS, CUTE and LEES for 124 points.
29. Play BAVIN and AT for 22 points.
30. Play STEADY and QUINA for 42 points.
31. Play YIBBLES, STAGY, AI, PLUMB, LUNGE and US for 120 points.

32. Play ZILCH and ZOOLOGY for 118 points. Other high-scoring moves include ZANTE and ZINCITE for 72 points, ZOO and ZINKED for 72 points, ZORIL and ZOOLOGY for 108 points, and ZILCH and COD for 93 points.

33. Using ME already on the board, and using the blank as an R, play REMEDY and MATED, for 38 points.

34. Play HOGBACK and OZONES for 115 points.

35. Using the blank as a C, and using an A of AIA, play WHACKY for 46 points.

36. Play NEUTRAL and RATE (or RATA) for 65 points.

37. Using the A of ZAX, play KART, KA, MOR and MOOT for 27 points.

38. Using the O of AEON, play THORP, TANA and HI for 35 points. If the E of AEON or the first E of EPEE were in slightly different places, then the word PLETHORA could be played.

39. Play ZANJERO and SOFTA for 107 points.

40. Using the blanks as a T and an A, play TARSOMETATARSUS for an incredible 455 points!

41. Play JOY and FY for 34 points.

42. Play QUADRAT for 34 points.

43. Play KHAT and KINGLET for 43 points.

44. Play YERD, WEY and COMER for 30 points.

45. Play PRIVATEERING for 57 points.

46. Play PAYMASTER and HAY for 91 points.

47. Play HO, HO and OYE, or THORN, or THUD, each of which scores 16 points.

48. Play LASERS (or LASSES) and JARVEYS for 54 points.

49. Play SEAS (or SETS), ELLS, WADE and BEYS for 29 points.

50. Using the A of ZOA, play JAUNTY for 32 points.

51. Using the C of CLAWING, play SECTORS, TA and OX for 59 points.

52. Parallel to METRES, and using the blank as an S, play VIMANAS, MI, THEM, TA, BARN, EA and PRINCESS for 120 points.

53. Play PTYXIS and BOWS for 87 points, retaining the blank on your rack.

54. Play JESTING and OBOES for 73 points.

55. Play VORTEX and OPEN for 90 points. OVERTAX can be made from the seven letters on your rack, but will not go down anywhere.

56. Play REVOLTS and FARE for 77 points.

57. Play WHEW, WIDE and WOVEN for 74 points.

58. Using the second D of ODD, play DYKE for 17 points.

59. In the top left-hand corner, play BENZYL, BEND and YON for 117 points. The seven-letter word BENZOYL can be played in several places, but, even with the 50-point bonus, it cannot beat 117 points.

60. Play ORGANIC, TAR, TEA and TIC for 87 points.

61. Play REPLA for 9 points.

62. Play WHISKY, HERRING, STARRING and YEARNING for 106 points.

63. Play MAYHEM, CHARM, SCARY and TRIPE for 77 points.

64. Play DIALYSE, NAY, IS and TE for 106 points.

65. Play either HERO, DOE and ATE or HERE, DEE and ATE, for 25 points.

66. Using the R of EWER, the second A of RANA, and the E of COME, play BAREFACED for 84 points.

67. Using the U of UNDER, play QUOTHA and AID for 80 points.

68. Play ZENITH, EASTERN, IRID and HEARTH for 91 points.

69. Using the V of CHIV, play DEVIANTS for 167 points.

70. Using the blank as an H, play SEVENTH, EH and BASEST for 91 points.

71. Play VIVA and ATE for 37 points.

72. Play DOZENTH, FINO and FINE for 112 points.

73. Play GAWP and BEG for 24 points.

74. Using the M of PROEM and the R of EPICURE, play SCRAMBLER and FAB for 88 points.

75. Using TE already on the board, play WHEEZE and TEW for 63 points.

76. Play AZOTHS and JACKS for 60 points.

77. Play SUNSETS, SHARP, NEARLY, ERODE and SWAN for 97 points.

78. Using PHO already on the board, play PHONOGRAPH for 96 points.

79. Play CROWD and RAYAH for 33 points.

80. Play FORCERS and FLAX for 80 points.

81. Play STAPPLE for 22 points.

82. Play APIARIST and EA for 24 points.

83. Play DANCERS, LID, AGO and TEN for 81 points.

84. Play BARONETCY and FAIRY for 81 points.

85. Play ETHANOL and JAKE for 79 points.

86. Using the M of MINED, play METHANOL for 78 points.

87. Play QUINATE, MENU and PARE for 132 points.

88. Using the As of AN and ANTE, play KA and KART for 34 points.

89. Play HOW, REH and WHOW for 44 points.

90. Using the J of JEE, play NYMPHO and JO for 66 points.

91. Play NASTIER, FA, ES, AT and YETI for 85 points.

92. Play EM, MY and AY for 28 points.

93. Play WALTZ, OW and AIA for 61 points.

94. Play FILMIC and TIBIAL for 42 points, retaining the blank on your rack.

95. Play WHARVES, OW and PATH for 98 points.

96. Play REDSKIN and CATERS for 30 points.

97. Play TICKER and UT for 47 points.

98. Using the S of NEEDLES, play ARSHINES for 94 points.

99. Play MAZILY, THEM, ERA and PERI for 76 points.

100. Using ATE already on the board, and using the blank as an L, play TRUNCATELY and DENT for 128 points.

101. Play EMBOX and TAX for 60 points.

102. Play HAD and HI for 28 points; or play OBI, BAD and OW for 28 points also.

103. Play KAZOO, KNOW, AE, ZO and ON for 94 points.

104. Play ZEBRA, ZOON, EGAD, BEL, RE and AS for 92 points.

105. Using the Y of BOOZY, play LYMPH for 45 points.

106. Play RHABDOM parallel to AILERON, making the vertical words RACHE, HI, ALONG, BE, DRUMLY, OON and MNA, all for 118 points.

107. Using the I of JINXES, play BRAID and DEE for 26 points.

108. Play FAIREST and TROUBLER for 88 points.

109. Play FRENZY and SOOTY for 90 points.

110. Play SHOED, SH and TO for 32 points.

111. Play HOPED, HAIRY and DA for 69 points; or play DOZE and DAIRY for 69 points also.

112. Play SQUALOR and RASTER for 93 points.

113. Using the R of ER, play WETHER and VOLE for 55 points.

114. Play ENTHRAL, YAWN, EAT and EH for 88 points.

115. Using the blank as a V, play AQUAVIT, PAWA and GELT for 138 points.

116. Using the E of SQUIRE, play WE and WHY for 29 points.

117. Play FLYPED and VATTED for 30 points.

118. Play SINTERY and YULE for 104 points.

119. Play BREASTPLATE for 88 points.

120. Play CHOUX and REX for 59 points.

121. Play ELEVENS, EL, TARE, RATE, and AGES for 91 points.

122. Play BREWS and ZOOS for 33 points.

123. Play SPIRTED and JOKER for 106 points.

124. Play DORHAWK and VALID for 101 points.

125. Play SISTERS and ELMS for 81 points.

126. Play CLAYEY, LARK, YOWL and Yare for 59 points.

127. Play LAXLY and GOY for 61 points.

128. Play VOODOO for 24 points.

129. Play KGOTLAS (yes, KGOTLAS!) and OVAL for 122 points.

130. Play WHY and HEFTY for 42 points.

131. Play DIRTIES and TAPED for 80 points.

132. Using the second A of AVA, play TALBOT and MAT for 42 points.

133. Play ELECTROPOSITIVE for 96 points.

134. Using BRA already on the board, CELEBRATOR for 78 points.

135. Play WHISK and LAAGERS for 38 points.

136. Using NA already on the board, play SNATCHILY, SPA and LAT for 83 points.

137. Play BILLOWY and SCARY for 106 points.

138. Play VISTA, SYE and TE for 40 points.

139. Play PAWK and PLED for 33 points.

140. Play PREFIX with the X on a double-letter-score square, retaining the blank on your rack. This scores 52 points.

141. Play OVARIES and DOZES for 85 points.

142. Play ERASION, OVERS, AI, TO and EN for 73 points.

143. Play SOREDIA and REND for 87 points. SOREDIA is the plural of SOREDIUM.

144. Play SODGERS and TACKS for 94 points.

145. Play BARKING (or BRAKING), UN and ERG for 90 points.

146. Play VODKA and SHARED for 44 points.

147. Play UNZIP and BEZ for 44 points.

148. Play BOXEN, OB, TO, OX and RE for 53 points.

149. Play COUNTERBALANCES for 116 points.

150. Play DINGED (or GIRDED) and BARE for 19 points.

151. Play STUDIER, AT, AYAHS and YU for 84 points.

152. Play HELIX and SWAMI for 48 points.

153. Play LISTED, LEA, IN and ST for 24 points.

154. Using the A of RASH, play WHACK for 35 points.

155. Play SALTER, AHA and LAH for 22 points. SALTER can be played vertically or horizontally.

156. Play ZED and REGALE for 32 points.

157. Play VARLETS, UT and ERS for 75 points.

158. Play FLICKING for 54 points.

159. Using the C of CLOVE, play PSYCHICS (with the Y on a double-letter-score square) for 98 points.

160. Play GRAVY and GLOVE for 39 points.

161. Play TOASTER and SKIDS for 76 points.

162. Play STYMING and NEVER for 74 points.

163. Using the F of CHIEF, play GRAFFITO for 80 points.

164. Play DOMICAL, COLD, FARM and GAVEL for 139 points.

165. Play HOAXED and BE for 75 points.

166. Play POLKA and HEMP for 56 points.

167. Play ANGUISH, TAI, TONS and FAH for 79 points.

168. Play JUNGLY and CHARY for 63 points.

169. Play GED and EMEU for 16 points.

170. Play CRWTH and PITH for 59 points.

171. Play CREDITS, MANIAC and WIND for 99 points.

172. Play ACHY and AX for 29 points.

173. Using the I of SKIFF, play YACHTING for 96 points.

174. Using MAD already on the board, and the Y of KEY, play YEN and MADE for 14 points.

175. Play FROWZY and HALLOW for 68 points.

176. Play ABRUPTLY for 45 points.

177. Play GRIPE and DIVERSE for 57 points.

178. Play EERIEST and TRIPE for 77 points.

179. Play THYMY for 40 points. The second Y must be on a double-letter-score square.

180. Using any of: the first E of RELATE, the first E of ELOPE, the E of PRETTY and the E of WOEFUL, play THYREOID for 80 points.

181. Play VULNING and COON for 100 points.

182. Play AXED and BAND for 35 points.

183. Play ZHO and HERO for 42 points.

184. Play PAGAN and HEAVEN for 30 points.

185. Play ECONUTS and TRAINEES for 104 points.

186. Play MASKED and VIOLATED for 41 points.

187. Using the V of GRAVE, play DOVETAIL for 78 points.

188. Play RITZY and BEZ for 52 points.

189. Play FAIRY and YEN for 33 points.

190. Play STYRENE, FAIRS, HAIRY, AN and BARE for 131 points.

191. Using the A of ALE, play DRACHMAI for 82 points.

192. Play SLEWING, COBS and HALLOW for 127 points.

193. Play COWPOX and OTIC for 78 points.

194. Play QUAYS for 54 points.

195. Using the blank as an O, play SNOWCAP and GRITS for 107 points.

196. Play VIZY and REV for 58 points.

197. Play ABJECT and ALIGHT for 50 points.

198. Play CLIMAX and FARM for 59 points.

199. Play SLITHER and MAXIMS for 79 points.

200. Using the blank as a V, play VITRAUX, JOT and TEA for 105 points.

Words Not in The Official Scrabble® Players Dictionary

Most of the puzzles and solutions in this collection use words that can be found in *The Official Scrabble® Players Dictionary*, published by G & C Merriam, the publishers of the authoritative Merriam-Webster dictionaries; however, there are some words used in the puzzles and solutions that don't appear in *The Official Scrabble® Players Dictionary*. These other words, taken from a variety of other dictionaries, are included in the list that follows. The list indicates the part of speech of each word, any derivative forms, and a brief definition. The format used here is similar to that used in *The Official Scrabble® Players Dictionary*.

ABBA n pl -S aba
AIA n pl -S ayah
AMELIA n pl -S a medical condition where limbs are absent
ANAN interj - used to express failure to understand
ANN n pl -S a half-yearly stipend
ARSHINE n pl -S archine
BAREFACED adj with the face uncovered
BARONETCY n pl -CIES the rank of baronet
BAVIN n pl -S a fagot of brushwood
BEZ n pl BEZZES part of a deer's horn
BIZ n pl BIZZES business
BOH interj - used to startle someone
BOR n pl -S neighbor

BOXEN adj like boxwood
BREASTPLATE n pl -S a piece of armor
BWAZI n pl -S an African shrub
CAGOULE n pl -S a lightweight anorak
CAMERATED adj chambered
CELEBRATOR n pl -S one who celebrates
CHA n pl -S tea
CHAL n pl -S fellow
CHIV v CHIVVED, CHIVVING, CHIVS to knife
CHOU n pl CHOUX a cabbage
COR n pl -S a Hebrew measure
COUNTERBALANCE v -ED, -ING, -S to act against with equal weight
COZE v COZED, COZING, COZES to chat
DIV n pl -S an evil Persian spirit
DOD v DODDED, DODDING, DODS to clip
DOH n pl -S do, the musical tone
DSO n pl -S zho
DZO n pl -S zho
EA n pl -S a river
ECONUT n pl -S a person concerned about the environment
EE n pl EEN eye
EGGLER n pl -S a dealer in eggs
ELECTROPOSITIVE adj carrying a positive charge
EMBOX v -ED, -ING, -ES to set in a box
EOAN adj pertaining to dawn
ERIC n pl -S a blood-fine in Irish law
ESNE n pl -S a domestic slave
ESTOC n pl -S a short sword
EUOI interj - used to express Bacchic frenzy
FAB adj FABBER, FABBEST excellent
FAH n pl -S fa, the musical tone
FINO n pl -S a dry sherry
FLYPE v FLYPED, FLYPING, FLYPES to strip back
FY interj - fie
GATEAU n pl -TEAUS or -TEAUX a rich cake
GAUNT v -ED, -ING, -S to yawn
GAWP v -ED, -ING, -S to gape
GEN v GENNED, GENNING, GENS to learn
GIF conj if
GIO n pl -S a creek
GREVE n pl -S greave

GU n pl -S a violin used in Shetland
HOA v HOAED, HOAING, HOAS to stop
IDE n pl -S a fish
IO n pl IOS a cry of joy
IRID n pl -S iris
ITA n pl -S a palm
JAK n pl -S a tree of the East Indies
JIZ n pl JIZZES a wig
KGOTLA n pl -S an assembly of tribal elders in Botswana
KY n/pl cows
LAH n pl -S la, the musical tone
LATHEN adj long and thin
LEV n pl LEVA the monetary unit of Bulgaria
LIONEL n pl -S a small lion
LOY n pl -S a spade
MAK n pl -S make
MEGAJOULE n pl -S one million joules
MEU n pl -S spignel, a plant
MNA n pl -S a Greek weight
MO adj more
MOINEAU n pl -S a bastion to protect a fortification
MOTETT n pl -S motet
NACRITE n pl -S a clay mineral
NAZIR n pl -S an official of various kinds
OB n pl -S an objection
OCH interj - used to express impatience
ONCER n pl -S a £1 note
ONER n pl -S a unique person or thing
OO n pl OOS wool
OON n pl -S an oven
OU interj - ow
OYE n pl -S a grandchild
PAWA n pl -S an edible shellfish
PAWK n pl -S a trick
PAYMASTER n pl -S one who pays workmen
PEC n pl -S a photoelectric cell
PHENIC adj of benzene
PHO interj - faugh
PHONOGRAPH n pl -S a gramophone
PHUT n pl -S a dull sound
PIARIST n pl -S a member of a religious congregation
PRIVATEER v -ED, -ING, -S to cruise in a private vessel

PTYXIS n pl PTYXES the folding of each individual leaf in a bud
PUKER n pl -S an emetic
QUIN n pl -S a quintuplet
QUINA n pl -S quinine
QUIPO n pl -S a contrivance of knotted cords
RACHE n pl -S a dog
RAGG n pl -S a rough hard stone
RANA n pl -S a prince
RAUN n pl -S a female fish
REH n pl -S an efflorescence of sodium salts in Indian soil
REPLUM n pl REPLA a fruit partition
RIPECK n pl -S a pole used to moor a punt
ROK n pl -S roc
RUMLY adv in an odd manner
SCRAMBLER n pl -S one who scrambles
SEZ v a variant spelling of "says"
SINTERY adj pertaining to a sinter
SNATCHILY adv in a snatchy manner
SNOOKER v -ED, -ING, -S to get the better of
SODGER n pl -S soldier
SOREDIUM n pl -DIA a reproductive body in lichens
SPARTAN adj hardy
ST interj - used to attract someone's attention
STAPPLE n pl -S a tobacco-pipe stem
STYME v STYMED, STYMING, STYMES to peer
SUPREMO n pl -S a supreme head
SYE v SYED, SYING, SYES to strain
TAAL n the Afrikaans language
TAI n pl -S a Japanese fish
TALBOT n pl-S a hound
TANA n pl -S a police station in India
TARAMASALATA n pl -S a Greek dish
TARSOMETATARSUS n pl -TARSI a bird's shank-bone
TE n pl TIS ti, the musical tone
TREEN adj wooden
TROUSSEAU n pl -SEAUS or -SEAUX a bride's outfit
TRUNCATELY adv in a truncate manner
UG v UGGED, UGGING, UGS to loathe
ULE n pl -S a rubber tree
ULTRACENTRIFUGE n pl -S a high-speed centrifuge
UNALIST n pl -S a holder of one benefice

UNROUGED adj not rouged
UR interj - used to fill a gap in speech
URE n pl -S an eighth of a mark
UVA n pl -S a grape
VAE n pl -S a creek
VALI n pl -S a governor
VIMANA n pl -S a temple gate
VITRAIL n pl VITRAUX stained glass
VIZY n pl VIZIES a careful look
VOL adj two wings displayed and joined at the base
VULN v -ED, -ING, -S to wound
WARRANTABLENESS n pl -ES the state of being justifiable
WEY n pl -S a measure of weight
WHOW interj - used to express deploration
WOG n pl -S a foreigner
YERD v -ED, -ING, -S to bury
YIBBLES adv perhaps
YLEM n pl -S a prime substance
YO n pl YOS a cry calling for effort
YU n pl YUS precious jade
YUG n pl -S one of the Hindu ages of the world
ZANJERO n pl -S a canal superintendent
ZANTE n pl -S a tree
ZEBUB n pl -S a fly
ZEL n pl -S an Oriental cymbal
ZHO n pl -S a hybrid cattle
ZINKED v a variant spelling of 'zinced'
ZINKING v a variant spelling of 'zincing'
ZO n pl ZOS zho

Gyles Brandreth

At thirty-five, Gyles Brandreth is one of Britain's most prolific and successful authors, having sold over eight million copies of his many books. A dozen of his children's titles have appeared in the United States and his other books published in America include *The Joy of Lex, More Joy of Lex, The Puzzle Mountain,* and *Great Theatrical Disasters.* Since 1981 his weekly "Alphabet Soup" column has been widely syndicated throughout the U.S. and Canada.

Born in 1948 and educated at Oxford University (where he was a Scholar at New College and, like several British Prime Ministers before him, President of the Oxford Union), Gyles Brandreth is also a journalist who has written for most of Britain's top newspapers and magazines, a broadcaster who has made over a thousand appearances on radio and TV, a theatrical producer with three London hits to his credit, the founder of the British championships with respect to the Scrabble® Brand Crossword Game, a former European Monopoly Champion, and the holder of the world record for the longest-ever after-dinner speech—twelve and a half hours!

He has lived in Hollywood, Baltimore, Washington, D.C., and New York, but now lives in London with his wife, who is also a writer, and their three children, who all have unique English names: Benet, Saethryd, and Aphra.

According to the *Scottish Sunday Post*, "Gyles Brandreth is the most likeable genius I've ever met!" According to the *London Daily Mail*, "Gyles Brandreth is the sort of person that a breakfast cereal company would give their right arm for. He's bursting with vigour, fizzing with happiness, sizzling with vim and *Cosmopolitan* magazine once picked him as one of England's most eligible bachelors, though he was actually married at the time." According to the *London Sun*, "Gyles Brandreth is a writer, talker, wit and diversified character with a bowling-over effect on anyone he meets."